Next-Generation Media: The Global Shift

A Report of the Forum on Communications and Society

Richard P. Adler
Rapporteur

THE ASPEN INSTITUTE

Communications and Society Program
Charles M. Firestone
Executive Director
Washington, DC
2007

To purchase additional copies of this report, please contact:

The Aspen Institute
Publications Office
P.O. Box 222
109 Houghton Lab Lane
Queenstown, Maryland 21658
Phone: (410) 820-5326
Fax: (410) 827-9174
E-mail: publications@aspeninstitute.org

For all other inquiries, please contact:

The Aspen Institute
Communications and Society Program
One Dupont Circle, NW
Suite 700
Washington, DC 20036
Phone: (202) 736-5818
Fax: (202) 467-0790

Charles M. Firestone	Patricia K. Kelly
Executive Director	*Assistant Director*

Contents

APPENDIX

Foreword

For over a decade the Aspen Institute Communications and Society Program has convened its CEO-level Forum on Communications and Society (FOCAS) to address specific issues relating to the impact of communications media on societal institutions and values. These small, invitation-only roundtables have addressed educational, democratic, and international issues with the aim of making recommendations to policy-makers, businesses and other institutions to improve our society through policies and actions in the information and communications sectors.

In the summer of 2006 the forum took a different turn. It is clear there is a revolution affecting every media business, every consumer or user of media, and every institution affected by media. In a word, everyone. FOCAS sought to define the paradigm changes underway in the media, and to identify some of the significant repercussions of those changes on society.

"Next Generation Media" was a three-day meeting among leaders from new media (e.g., Google, craigslist, and Second Life) and mainstream media (e.g., *The New York Times* and *Time*), from business, government, academia and the non-profit sector, all seeking a broad picture of where the digital revolution is taking us.

This report of the meeting, concisely and deftly written by Richard Adler, a longtime consultant in the field, weaves insights and anecdotes from the roundtable into a coherent document supplemented with his own research and data to form an accessible, coherent treatment of this very topical subject.

The specific goals of the 2006 forum were to examine the profound changes ahead for the media industries, advertisers, consumers and users in the new attention economy; to understand how the development and delivery of content are creating new business models for commercial and non-commercial media; and to assess the impact of these developments on global relations, citizenship and leadership.

The report thus examines the growth of the Internet and its effect on a rapidly changing topic: the impact of new media on politics, business, society, culture, and governments the world over. The report also sheds light on how traditional media will need to adapt to face the competition of the next generation media.

Beginning, as the Forum did, with data from Jeff Cole's Center for the Digital Future at the University of Southern California, Adler documents the increasing popularity of the Internet for information, entertainment and communication. Users are increasingly generating and contributing content to the web and connecting to social networks. They are posting comments, uploading pictures, sharing videos, blogging and vlogging, chatting through instant messages or voice over Internet (VoIP), or emailing friends, business colleagues, neighbors and even strangers. As Cole observes, "Traditional media informed people but didn't empower them." New media do.

The report describes three of the Internet's most successful ventures—Wikipedia, Second Life, and craigslist. Wikipedia is a prime example of how an Internet platform allows its users to generate content and consume it. As a result of "wiki" software technology anyone can contribute or edit existing information free of cost. Second Life, a virtual world, sells virtual real estate where subscribers, in avatar form, can conduct conversations, go to lectures, even create a business. Craigslist, a predominantly free online classified site with listings in every major city in the United States, has become so popular that it is posing a significant threat to newspapers as it competes with their classified ad revenues.

As a result of these and other new media phenomena, not the least being Google and Yahoo, print publications are wrestling with new business models that could entail fundamentally restructuring the way they operate. For instance, reporters are now expected to report a story on multiple media platforms and discuss them online with readers. Newspaper publisher Gannett is exploring the incorporation of user-generated news or "citizen-journalism" into its news pages.

In an era of abundant choices marketers have an even greater challenge to figure out how best to appeal to consumers. The report explores how marketers, e.g., of Hollywood movies or pomegranate juice, are moving from traditional or mainstream media to viral and other marketing techniques.

For much of the world, the mobile phone rather than the computer is the most important communications device. Users depend on their phones to send and receive messages, pictures, and download information rather than just talk. In developing countries mobile phones are having an exceptional impact, penetrating regions which are not being serviced by land lines. Thus we are seeing new uses daily for this increased connectivity, from reporting election results in emerging democracies to opposing authoritarian governments in order to bring about new democracies.

Meanwhile, the report discusses the need for the United States to develop a new form of public diplomacy rather than the traditional top-down approach to communicating to foreign citizens. This topic has been a recurring theme at FOCAS conferences the past few years, this year calling for more citizen diplomacy—that is, more person-to-person contact across borders through uses of the new media. Indeed, Peter Hirshberg suggested that American leaders should listen more to the outside world to effectively manage what he called "Brand America."

Finally, after acknowledging the detrimental effects that new technologies can bring about, the report discusses what role those technologies could play in expanding freedom and opportunity for the next generation. As a conclusion, FOCAS co-chair Marc Nathanson proposed adding a ninth goal to the United Nations Millennium Goals, namely, "to provide access to appropriate new technologies."

Acknowledgments

I would like to thank FOCAS co-chairs Marc Nathanson and Reed Hundt whose extensive inputs contributed to this meeting's special success. I want to thank each of the members of the FOCAS for contributing their time, attention and financial support for this important activity. Finally, I want to acknowledge and thank Richard Adler for tying the dialogue into a well written and coherent report and, with the help of Peter Hirshberg, putting an interactive version of this document online; and Mridulika Menon and Tricia Kelly, both of the Communications and Society Program, for producing the conference and this report.

Charles M. Firestone
Washington, D.C.
February 2007

Next-Generation Media: The Global Shift

Richard P. Adler

Next-Generation Media:
The Global Shift

Richard P. Adler

The Internet is old news. But its 700 million users are changing business and society
so fast it's sometimes hard to keep up, and the revolution is just beginning.

- "Life in a Connected World," *Fortune*, June 28, 2006

Introduction

A decade ago the Internet was still a novelty. Only a minority of
Americans went online regularly, and the rate of global penetration was
even smaller.

Today the Internet is so pervasive that we often take its presence for
granted, thinking of it as "old news." It has become part of the daily life
of a majority of Americans who rely on it as an almost indispensable
tool for both business and personal life: a vital communications link, an
important source of news and political information, a convenient channel for distributing digital content of all types (including software,
music, photos, and videos), and a robust marketplace for electronic
commerce (e-commerce).

With nearly four out of five Americans now going online regularly,
the Internet has taken its place among older media as an important
medium in its own right, offering users an enormous range of choices.
It provides instant access to a seemingly unlimited array of content that
reflects almost every conceivable interest, perspective, and point of
view. Search for almost any topic on Google, and you will get thousands, tens of thousands, even millions of references to that subject.

Because access to so many choices is now so easy, the Internet and
powerful search engines such as Google have made it much simpler for
individuals to find the content they want rather than the content any
publisher might decide to offer. Similarly, consumers now have access to
so much information about products and services that advertisers have
much less control over the messages about their products that reach
their customers. One of the most significant effects of the Internet has

3

been to empower individuals and to diminish the power of the gate-keepers who formerly exercised control over the media environment.

The Internet has done more than expand the menu of choices available to the typical user, however. Unlike earlier media, the Internet is interactive, allowing users not only to access content created by others but also to create and publish their own content, using a variety of tools that are available online. Through blogs, wikis, social networks, and virtual worlds, the Internet has empowered millions of people to express their opinions, share their knowledge, and project their identities into the world. In short, the Internet has emerged both as a *medium* that has greatly expanded access to multiple sources of information and as a *platform* that has enabled individuals to become producers as well as consumers of online content.

The Internet empowers the individual and diminishes the power of the gatekeepers.

Finally, the fundamental architecture of the Internet allows individuals to connect directly with other users without the need for any intermediary. Some of the largest sites on the Web, such as eBay, Friendster, and MySpace, have grown by facilitating connections between people with common interests. This flowering of peer-to-peer communications may be the most disruptive innovation of the Internet both economically and socially.

To consider the global significance of the growth of the Internet, particularly of the "next generation" media that have emerged on the Internet in the past few years, the Aspen Institute Forum on Communications and Society (FOCAS) met in the summer of 2006 in Aspen, Colorado. The meeting brought together representatives of older media—broadcasting, magazines, newspapers, film, and recorded music—with some of the pioneers of new media to explore the new world of the Internet and its impact on individuals, politics, and global relationships. The participants also examined how traditional media have attempted to respond to this new upstart, recognizing that they will have to redefine their roles if they are going to remain relevant.

From Mass to Personal, From Push to Pull

Freedom of the press, as A.J. Liebling once observed, belongs to the person who owns one. Traditional media might have informed their audiences, but they did not, except in very limited ways, offer their readers, listeners, or viewers the opportunity to express themselves. Newspapers and magazines, radio and television, film and recorded music are all essentially one-to-many media. In each case, the ability to create appealing content has been restricted to a relatively small number of highly trained professionals. The costs of creating and distributing high-quality content, like the rewards for popular content, have been high.

The trend through modern times has been to expand the range of media choices available to the public. The introduction of FM radio and UHF television effectively doubled the number of stations in a single market, and the arrival of cable television and satellite radio increased the number of choices almost exponentially. The introduction of home recording and playback devices freed viewers from the need to watch a particular program at a particular time, allowing them to become their own programmers. Even in the world of print, where the economics of publishing have not changed as dramatically as they have in the world of electronic media, niche publishing has led to the creation of scores of magazines tailored to individual interests, while general-interest magazines have struggled to survive.

The rise of the Internet has greatly accelerated this trend. Unlike traditional media, the Internet places virtually no limits on the range of choices to which it can provide access. As a general rule, any content that is published on the Internet is instantly available to any user anywhere in the world. Even cable television or satellite radio increased the number of choices from a handful of channels to hundreds; the Internet has provided access to millions of channels of content.

At the same time, the cost of the tools of digital content production has decreased steadily. Whereas a printing press remains a costly and therefore scarce good, personal computers have become so inexpensive that they are affordable even for individuals of fairly modest means. Moreover, thanks to the spread of the Internet, that digital content can now be made accessible to the entire world at little cost.

In such an environment of superabundant choice, one of the biggest challenges for users is simply being able to find the content that is of interest to them. One of the quintessential Internet success stories has been Google, a company that grew in a remarkably short period of time from an academic research project into an economic powerhouse and a genuine cultural phenomenon by providing one simple function: a "search engine" that was better than others at helping users find the content they were looking for.

The implications of this vast expansion of choice were addressed at the 2005 Aspen Institute Roundtable on Information Technology and explored in the subsequent report, *When Push Comes to Pull,* by David Bollier. The conclusion of that meeting was that the lowered costs of production and distribution and the resulting increase in choice that this has brought about are causing a far-reaching shift from a "push" economy to a "pull" economy. According to Bollier:

> A "push economy"—the kind of economy that was responsible for mass production in the 20th century— is based on anticipating consumer demand and then making sure that the needed resources are brought together at the right place, at the right time, for the right people.... By contrast, a "pull economy"—the kind of economy that appears to be materializing in online environments—is based on open, flexible production platforms that use networking technologies to orchestrate a broad range of resources.... Small niches of consumer demand long dismissed or patronized by sellers are a growing market force unto themselves. They can increasingly induce sellers to develop specialized products and services to serve narrow and time-specific market demands.[1]

The shift from "push" to "pull" extends well beyond the creation of digital media. Industrial companies that exemplify this new model include Toyota's "lean manufacturing" process, Dell Computer's "build-to-order" production model, Chinese apparel company Li & Fung's ability to draw on a network of 7,500 partners, and Cisco Systems' global network of 40,000 specialized business partners that can customize its products for individual customers. As these examples suggest, success in a "pull" economy requires companies to organize and operate in dramatically different ways from the ways traditional companies operate. These new models, Bollier notes, "seem to be especially well suited to enterprising companies, developing nations (such as India and China), and the younger generation."

Google's Ad-Words

Google's Ad-Words is a classic example of a "push" business that is flourishing on the Internet. Google's search engine had already become wildly popular before the company identified any strategies for turning that popularity into revenue. The company's founders were adamantly opposed to compromising the integrity of its search results by allowing advertisers to buy more favorable rankings. The solution—first suggested by a company employee—was to offer advertiser-supported searches linked to specific search terms, or keywords, but to display the results of these paid searches separately from Google's main listings in relatively unobtrusive text listings that were clearly identified as paid ads.

This approach preserved the integrity of Google's search results and provided users with ads directly linked to the search terms they entered—and therefore, presumably, topics of interest to them. In addition, advertisers who purchase particular keywords only pay Google when a user actually clicks on a link in a search-related ad. How much advertisers pay for these "clicks" is based on the amount they are willing to bid for a high-priority listing. (Advertisers generally believe that they must be listed in one of the top three sponsored positions on Google, and they generally are willing to pay a premium to assure one of these top listings.)

The result of this scheme is a highly efficient form of advertising that responds directly to the interests of users and—in theory, at least—enables advertisers to pay only for potential customers who are sufficiently interested in their offerings to seek them out. According to Lynda Resnick, creator of POM Wonderful pomegranate products and an experienced marketer of other products, keyword search is "the greatest marketing technique ever."

Google's Ad-Words have been an impressive economic success: The fees they generate now account for a majority of the company's revenues.

As significant as this shift may be, the 2006 FOCAS meeting identified a trend that may be even more far-reaching. The Internet is not simply expanding users' choices; it is blurring the line between users and producers. In other words, an increasing portion of Internet content is being created not by publishing companies or specialized entities but by groups of ordinary users who regard the Internet as a medium for personal expression or as a means for communicating and collaborating with their peers. This trend goes beyond suggesting a new way to organize a business venture; it represents a direct challenge to the primacy of market-based production with a new model of "social production."

The State of the Internet

For the past six years, the Center for the Digital Future at the University of Southern California's Annenberg School for Communication has been conducting an annual survey to track how Americans are using the Internet and other media. The results of the most recent survey, released in December 2006, provide evidence of the extent to which the Internet has now become part of everyday life for most Americans.[2] The survey shows that while users are becoming more dependent on the Internet for information, they are becoming more discerning about the information they find online. The survey also found that the Internet is becoming an increasingly powerful political force, a means for individuals to participate in online communities that are important to them. Finally, an increasing number of users are posting their own content online, as well as using the Internet to seek out information created by others.

Among the key findings from USC's 2007 survey (which reports on data collected in 2006), according to Jeffrey Cole, director of the Center, are the following:

- More than three-quarters of Americans older than age 12 (77.6 percent) now are on the Internet. The average home user now spends 14 hours per week online—an increase from 9.4 hours a week in 2000 and 13.3 hours a week in 2005 (see Figure 1).

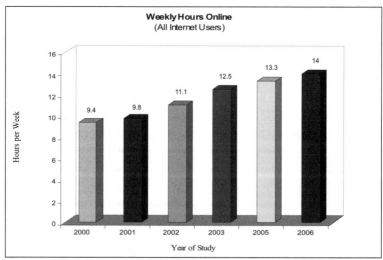

Figure 1: Trend in Hours Spent Online, 2000-2006

Source: 2007 Digital Future Report, USC Annenberg School Center for the Digital Future

- The Internet is now the most important single source of information and entertainment for a majority of users. In 2006, nearly two-thirds of Internet users (65.8 percent) considered the Internet to be a very important or extremely important source of information and entertainment for them, compared to 56.3 percent in 2005.

- Although Americans are spending more time online, they are growing more cautious about trusting information they find on the Internet. In 2006, just more than half of all users (55.2 percent) say they believe that most or all of the information online is reliable and accurate. This finding represents an increase from 48.8 percent of users who trusted all online information in 2005, although it is below the peak of 58 percent who trusted most online information in 2001.

- The way people are using the Internet is changing. Just as television viewers shifted their viewing pattern from simply turning on the TV to watch a specific program in the early days of the medium to turning on the TV to "see what's on," Internet users are increasingly going online without a specific destination in mind. As of 2006, nearly three-quarters of Internet users (74 percent) reported that they sometimes (44.1 percent) or often (29.9 percent) went online without a specific destination.

- One reason for this shift almost certainly is the growing popularity of always-on broadband, which makes accessing the Internet much easier and quicker than a dial-up connection. The most recent USC survey found that nearly half of home users (48.3 percent) now access the Internet via broadband, and the number of users who still rely on a telephone connection dropped from 61.5 percent in 2004 to 37 percent in 2006.

The USC survey also showed that Americans are becoming more active participants in and contributors to the Internet rather than just being passive consumers of online content:

- The Internet is increasingly being used as an important tool in business as well as an enjoyable personal resource. The percentage of workers who say that having access to the Internet at work makes them more productive has increased steadily over the six years the USC survey has been conducted, reaching a level of 69.7 percent of workers in 2006.

- The percentage of users who posted their own content on the Internet—either by maintaining their own website, keeping a blog, or posting photos online—has grown rapidly. The most popular activity is posting photos to the Web, which 23.6 percent of users now do, compared to 15.7 percent in 2005 and 11 percent in 2004. Similarly, the percentage of users who keep a blog has grown from 3.2 percent in 2003 to 7.4 percent in 2006, and those who maintain their own website has increased from 8.5 percent in 2003 to 12.5 percent in 2006.

Traditional media informed people but didn't *empower* them.

In reviewing these findings, Cole notes that the impact of the Internet on users is different from that of previous media in a critical way. Traditional media *informed* people but didn't *empower* them. While this informed characteristic initially was true of the Internet as well, today nearly half (47 percent) of Internet users say that they feel empowered by the Internet. In politics, for example, phenomena such as MoveOn.org, which provided many people with a new sense of involvement in the political process, demonstrate the extent of this impact.

The desire for empowerment extends to other realms as well. It is evident, for example, in the millions of people who have started blogs to share their opinions with the world at large. It also shows up in the healthcare arena; many patients use the Internet to research their medical problems and are determined to use what they learn to be part of the team that is responsible for their treatment. It is vividly evident in commerce: many consumers would not think of buying a car today without first doing research online about reliability records and actual dealer costs.

The desire for empowerment also is evident in the way teenagers routinely use the Internet to download content that appeals to them (often without asking permission or paying a royalty to anyone), move it from platform to platform, transform it, and repost it for others to enjoy. With millions of individuals now posting content online that is likely to be of interest only to themselves and a small group of friends and family members, Andy Warhol's old maxim that "everyone will get to be famous for 15 minutes" may have to be revised to say that, on the Internet, "everyone will have 15 megabytes of fame" or, more precisely, "everyone will be famous among 15 people."

USC's Cole noted that in developed countries such as the United Kingdom, Sweden, Singapore, and South Korea, usage is very similar to that in the United States. In China, however, the pattern is very different. Just 10 percent of the population in that country is currently online; of those who are online, 70 percent go online from public Internet cafes. In contrast, in the United States, nearly two-thirds of users (66.2 percent) now access the Internet from home, compared to 46.9 percent in 2001. Whereas Americans enjoy unlimited access to the Internet for a flat monthly fee, Chinese users pay an hourly fee for Internet access. Another difference between the two countries is that Americans use the Internet for a wide range of purposes, including work and professional interests, whereas Chinese users tend to use the Internet primarily for recreational and social purposes such as gaming and dating. (In many developing countries, including China, the use of cell phones for text as well as voice communications is more widespread than PC-based Internet use. In China, for example, more than one-quarter of the population—more than 400 million people—now use cell phones, compared to just 10 percent who use the Internet.)

Life in Online Communities

One of the things the Internet does best is to allow people with common interests to find each other. This ability of the Internet to bring people together in communities of interest was recognized almost from the earliest days of the medium, when many so-called newsgroups were formed to enable people to share ideas about topics both serious (e.g., discussions of specific academic disciplines, religion, technology, and politics) and not-so-serious (e.g., hobbies, recreational travel, jokes, and humor). These groups existed primarily in the form of text-only bulletin boards where participants could read others' messages and add their own. Although the technology was relatively simple, many participants invested a considerable amount of time contributing to these discussions and keeping their communities functioning.

Today, online communities have gone mainstream. No longer just the province of early adopters, they are now an intrinsic part of some of the Internet's most popular sites. Yahoo! and Google provide free resources that support thousands of user-created communities. eBay, which claims millions of users, describes itself as a "community" that brings individuals with common interests together to buy and sell an almost endless variety of goods. CNET provides not only content generated by experts but also a home for a multiplicity of "forums" where users can get help with or exchange opinions about a wide range of technology-related topics. Social networking sites such as MySpace and FaceBook have become enormously popular meeting places for millions of young people.

Starting in 2005, the USC survey included questions designed to elicit information about participation in and attitudes toward online communities. The most recent survey found that more than two-thirds (67.2 percent) of people who participate in online communities say that these communities are very important (35.7 percent) or extremely important (31.5 percent) to them; just 2.5 percent say their online communities are not at all important to them. In addition, 43 percent of participants in online communities said that they "felt as strongly" about their online communities as they did about the real-world communities in which they participate. The importance of online communities to the people who participate in them is underscored by the fact that more than half of online community members (56.6 percent) log onto their communities at least once a day.

According to USC's research, many people participate in multiple online communities, not just a single community. Although there may be an upper bound to the number of different communities in which individuals can be active participants and not just visitors, no one currently seems to know what it is is.

Yochai Benkler, professor of law at Yale Law School and author of a new study, *The Wealth of Networks: How Social Production Transforms Markets and Freedom* (Yale University Press, 2006), suggested that one reason people are able to participate in a larger number of communities online than in the real world is that the "activation energy"—the cost in time, energy, and personal commitment—required to participate in an online community is substantially lower than in the real world. "There are a lot of things you can do in 20 minutes with online interactions," Benkler pointed out.

The Net, Community, and Traditional Media

The rise of the Internet has begun to have a measurable impact on older media—particularly on print media. A 2006 article in *The Economist* summarizes some of the problems besetting the newspaper industry:[3]

> Paid circulation is falling year after year. Papers are also losing their share of advertising spending. Classified advertising is quickly moving online. Jim Chisholm, of iMedia, a joint-venture consultancy with IFRA, a newspaper trade association, predicts that a quarter of print classified ads will be lost to digital media in the next ten years. Overall, says iMedia, newspapers claimed 36 percent of total global advertising in 1995 and 30 percent in 2005. It reckons they will lose another five percentage points by 2015.

To illustrate the challenge posed by the Internet to traditional media such as newspapers, Arthur Sulzberger, chairman of the New York Times Company and publisher of *The New York Times*, asked conference participants what they thought the biggest problem facing the Titanic was. Running into an errant iceberg, he said, was not the answer: Even if the ship had successfully crossed the Atlantic, it was already doomed by the first flight of a heavier-than-air craft that had taken place at Kitty Hawk 12 years before the Titanic's first voyage. The future of transatlantic travel would belong to aviation, not to ships, however magnificent they might be. The question that the owners of the Titanic should have been asking themselves was not how to build a better ship but how they could transform a steamship company into an airline company.

Sulzberger acknowledged that "it is now all about community" for newspapers as well as for the Internet. The question he and his print colleagues face, however, is how publications such as *The New York Times* "can become part of the conversation" that happens online. One response has been for the paper to stop publishing "generic information" such as stock tables and television listings because they can be more efficiently provided online than in a print publication (although Sulzberger noted ruefully that *The New York Times* got more angry responses from readers when it decided to stop publishing television listings than it did when it ran a controversial story about the National Security Agency's warrentless wiretapping activities).

Other publishers are taking even more far-reaching steps. For example, Gannett, which owns and operates 90 newspapers around the country including *USA Today*, announced that it is responding to the challenge posed by the Internet by "fundamentally restructuring" the way in which its papers operate. According to one report, the company is "radically changing the way its papers gather and present news by incorporating elements of reader-created 'citizen-journalism,' mining online community discussions for stories and creating Internet databases of calendar listings and other non-news utilities."[4] Under Gannett's new plan, newsrooms will become "information centers;" instead of being divided into traditional beat-oriented sections, they will be organized by functions such as public service, digital data, community conversation, local content, custom content, and multimedia.

> **"It is now all about community."**
>
> *Arthur Sulzberger*

One problem that Sulzberger believes has been exaggerated is the perception that newspaper readers are primarily older whereas younger people have forsaken print and are flocking to the Internet. Sulzberger noted that the average age of a *New York Times* reader is between 44 and 45 years, and this age has not increased in a decade—and the average age of today's Internet user also is 45.

News magazines face much the same challenge from the Internet as newspapers. James Kelly, the managing editor of Time Inc., explained that the magazines that have done best online have been those—such as *Real Simple, InStyle, This Old House, Sports Illustrated,* and *People*—that focus on topics around which online communities have already been formed. *Time* magazine faces the biggest problem in adapting to the Internet because it serves a broad, general audience and, as a weekly, lags behind the instant dissemination of news online even more than daily newspapers. *Time*'s dilemma is that it is not obvious who or what is the online community to which it most naturally appeals. The most logical online role that *Time* has been able to identify for itself is to provide "the interpretation of breaking news," which it does on CNN's online site, cnn.com. Kelly acknowledged, however, that this solution is less than ideal. Internet users, it turns out, prefer to watch video online rather than read text for news reporting and analysis. What remains to be seen is whether there is still a viable role for newsweeklies such as *Time* or if they will eventually suffer the same fate as previous general interest magazines such as *Life* and *Look*.

The film industry also has had difficulty in adapting to the new online world. According to Dan Glickman, president and chief executive officer (CEO) of the Motion Picture Association of America (MPAA), the industry has based its success on generating large audiences for "big releases." In that sense, Hollywood has been a classic "push" industry, and it has been challenged to adapt to the "pull" world of the Internet. The industry has primarily regarded digital online distribution of movies on the Internet as a threat to its traditional distribution channels. Nevertheless, there have been some success stories in which the industry has used the Internet to promote conventional movies, particularly offbeat films that appeal to specific special interest groups. Interest in "The Chronicles of Narnia," the film version of C.S. Lewis's Christian parable, was stimulated through promotion on a variety of religious Web sites. The "DaVinci Code" also was promoted on religious sites. The hit film "Talladega Nights," which is about stock car racing, was promoted through Web sites where NASCAR fans gathered, as well as through satellite radio channels.

The Internet clearly is creating a new environment—and new challenges—for marketers of all types of products. Peter Hirshberg, chairman and chief marketing officer of Technorati, argued that the challenge for marketers is not to choose between old media and new media but to figure out how to combine them most effectively. Hirshberg cited the example of Dove Soap, which launched a major print campaign around the theme of "real beauty" and simultaneously sponsored an online site, mentioned in the print ads, where women could talk about the campaign. The site attracted thousands of posts and helped to reinforce the print campaign.

Lynda Resnick, co-owner and vice-chairman of Roll International Corporation, also defended the continued relevance of old media in marketing contemporary brands such as Fiji Water and Pom Wonderful pomegranate juice. Resnick's company owns orchards that grow pomegranates and developed Pom Wonderful as a way of creating a wider market for this relatively esoteric crop (market research had shown that only 12 percent of Americans even know what a pomegranate is).[5] The company spent millions of dollars sponsoring medical research that documented the health benefits of pomegranate juice and millions more on introducing the new product when it launched the brand in 2002. One of the most effective vehicles the company used to build awareness of Pom was "unavoidable media" such as billboards and ads on buses. Special-interest magazines (such as those that focus on health and fitness) also worked well.

"The game changer is user-created content."

John Rendon

Resnick also noted that "[public relations] remains an unsung hero" in promoting brands: "If you have a newsworthy product, you can get news coverage" in new as well as in old media.

Jordan Greenhall, founder and CEO of DivX, a developer of media creation tools for the Internet, argued that the way companies should communicate with customers online is fundamentally different from the conventions of traditional media. The lesson marketers need to learn, Greenhall suggested, is the lesson Bill Murray had to learn in the movie "Groundhog Day." In the movie, Murray plays a television weatherman who is caught in a cycle in which he lives the same day over and over. In the first half of the movie, he tries to use his knowledge of what will happen that day to manipulate his world to get what he wants—including the affections of his attractive female producer. Each time, he fails to get what he wants. When he realizes that he can use his unique knowledge to help others and to truly participate in the community, however, he is freed from his time trap—and he gets the girl. The moral of the story for marketers is that they will be more successful when they give up their desire to control their customers and are willing to honestly join existing communities and participate fully in them.

Next-Generation Content: User-Generated Content and Social Networks

"The game changer," according to John Rendon, president of the Rendon Group, a global strategic communications consultancy, "is user-created content." This phenomenon is the most transformative innovation in communications since the invention of radio. From the perspective of most existing businesses, the Internet provides new channels for marketing their products, but at least to this point it has not fundamentally changed the way in which they operate.

As the initial discussion of the Internet and its impacts made increasingly clear, however, the Net is in some fundamental way different from previous media. Whereas virtually all existing mass media have concentrated control in the hands of a relatively small group of professional producers who are skilled in informing or entertaining vast audiences, the Internet has put the means of production in the hands of virtually every user. Anyone with access to the Internet who is willing to conform to a few simple, open protocols (e.g., TCP/IP) can create and publish content that in theory is available to anyone else who is connected to the Internet.

> **The Internet is not merely a *medium* but a *platform*.**
>
> *Yochai Benkler*

As a result of this decentralized architecture, the Internet breaks down the distinction between producers and consumers. Moreover, because of the continuously declining cost of almost all things digital, the cost of acquiring the tools needed to produce content on the Internet has become so low that millions of individuals can afford it.

As Yale Law School professor Yochai Benkler put it, the Internet is not merely a *medium* (that is, a channel for distributing content) but a *platform* that enables millions of individuals to become content producers as well as consumers. Unlike other media, no one owns the Internet, and no one controls it. A "platform," according to Benkler, is "a technical and organizational context in which a community can interact to achieve a specific purpose." In fact, some of the Internet's most successful enterprises have succeeded by developing and distributing Internet-based platforms that allow individuals to create their own content.

Among the Internet's most distinctive successes are resources that enabled groups of people to work together collaboratively and voluntarily in surprisingly effective ways.

Wikipedia

One of the best examples of how powerful and disruptive an Internet platform can be is Wikipedia, the online encyclopedia that Benkler describes as "one of the most successful collaborative enterprises that has developed in the first five years of the 21st century." Wikipedia depends on "wiki" technology—a software tool that allows groups of people to work together to create and edit documents:

> This platform enables anyone, including anonymous passersby, to edit almost any page in the entire project. It stores all versions, makes changes easily visible, and enables anyone to revert a document to any prior version as well as to add changes, small and large. All contributions and changes are rendered transparent by the software and database.[7]

The wiki concept initially was conceived as a means to facilitate collaboration among small work groups. The first wiki software was developed in 1994 by a computer scientist who wanted to create a convenient way for programmers to share techniques. In 2001, however, Jimmy Wales decided to use this tool for a broader, more ambitious purpose: to allow a group of strangers with no institutional connections to work together to create a true encyclopedia. In addition to making the software tool widely available online, Wales established a relatively small number of rules for contributors, including encouraging authors to strive toward an objective, factual style (rather than expressing a personal point of view). Perhaps most important, he developed a framework that makes updating, expanding, and correcting entries easy.

George W. Bush in Wikipedia

A good example of how Wikipedia operates—and the challenges it faces in maintaining the integrity of its content—is the entry on President George W. Bush. The article is more than 9,000 words in length and includes information about Bush's early life and political career, as well as detailed discussions of his first and second terms. Although one section of the entry covers "criticism and public perceptions" of the President and reports on changes in his overall approval rating, the article is written in a consciously neutral style.

Because the article is online, it can be kept continuously up to date. Because all content in Wikipedia is designed to be edited and re-edited by any visitor, however, the article on Bush has been subject to "vandalism," presumably committed by critics of the President. Thus, the article includes a note explaining that "editing of this article by anonymous or registered users is currently disabled."

The article on President Bush—like all articles in Wikipedia—includes several tabs at the top that provide additional perspectives on the content. The "discussion" tab provides access to an ongoing discussion of the article. In some cases, entries in this section challenge or seek clarification of specific statements in the article (asking, for example, "What is the source of this statement?"). The "history" tab provides a running account of all of the modifications made to the article. The ability to document and annotate Wikipedia's content provides a transparency to the editorial process that is generally absent from most print publications.

Wikipedia grew slowly at first but then began to expand rapidly. In its first year of operation, it attracted fewer than 500 contributors, who completed about 19,000 entries. By June 2005, however, nearly 50,000 contributors had written more than 1.6 million articles. Moreover, although Wikipedia is based in the United States, it has become a truly global phenomenon: Whereas 84 percent of all articles contributed in the first year were in English, by the middle of 2005 less than 40 percent were in English.

Wikipedia has proved to be highly popular. In July 2006 Wikipedia attracted 29.2 million visitors, which made it one of the 20 most-visited websites and one of the 10 fastest-growing sites on the Web.[8] Despite its success, Wikipedia has remained resolutely noncommercial. No one is paid to contribute content, and no one is charged to use it. None of the material is copyrighted. The site is operated by the Wikimedia Foundation and is supported primarily by user donations. The foundation had a 2005 operating budget of $739,200.

Critics have questioned the reliability of a product that is created by an amorphous group of anonymous nonprofessionals. Yet one of the strengths of Wikipedia is its ability to correct errors after they are identified. Former Secretary of State Madeleine Albright, principal of The Albright Group, noted at a previous Aspen conference that she had found inaccuracies in the Wikipedia entry about herself, and she was able to correct it on the spot.

Wikipedia can be disarmingly honest about its own shortcomings. In some cases, Wikipedia's editors take the initiative in pointing out that some of its entries are works in progress that may need additional work. For example, some entries carry notices addressed to users and contributors that say things such as, "This article or section may be confusing or unclear for some readers, and should be edited to rectify this. Please improve the article, or discuss the issue on the talk page."

In fact, Wikipedia has done quite well in terms of accuracy, compared with more traditional publications. An article published in the journal *Nature* in December 2005 compared 42 articles on scientific topics in Wikipedia with entries in the *Encyclopedia Britannica* and concluded that there was not much difference with regard to the accuracy of the articles.[9] Yet Wikipedia's timeliness, comprehensiveness, and editorial transparency are qualities that traditional publications cannot easily match. As Jordan Greenhall noted, Wikipedia "lays all of its cards on the table" and lets its users take responsibility for deciding what they believe and don't believe.

Second Life

In the 1992 science fiction novel *Snow Crash*, by Neal Stephenson, an unemployed pizza deliveryman is a hero in the Metaverse, an alternate world that exists only in cyberspace. While the deliveryman's daily life in the real world is mundane and dreary, his adventures in the virtual world of the Metaverse are the stuff of high drama.

In fact, virtual online worlds have been part of the Internet since its early days (see sidebar, "MUDS, MOOs, and WorldsAway"). When an avatar from Linden Lab's Second Life appeared on the cover of *Business Week* in March 2006, however, it signaled that virtual worlds had come of age. Second Life, introduced in 2003, is a complex, three-dimensional world populated by highly detailed avatars. According to Linden Lab's chief technology officer Cory Ondrejka, however, the secret of Second Life's success is not its graphic richness but its commitment to providing users with the ability to create and control much of the content of Second Life. Fully 70 percent of Second Life's participants are also content creators.[10]

MUDS, MOOs, and WorldsAway

The first online virtual worlds, known as multi-user domains (MUDs) and MUD object-oriented (MOOs) appeared on the Internet in the 1980s. These "worlds" existed only in the form of text, and the experience of visiting a MUD or MOO was something like interacting with a text novel. On entering (i.e., logging on to) the MUD, the user was presented with a text description of a physical environment, which might be a room in a mansion or an open field. Through a series of commands, the user explores the MUD. What made MUDs compelling, however, was that they were places where people could meet and interact with others. Participants could present themselves as they wished and experiment with different identities and roles. Although MUDs never achieved widespread popularity, a small group of early adopters used them to explore the potential for creating alternate worlds and alternate personas online.[11]

A decade later, in the 1990s, a new generation of graphic virtual worlds was introduced. In these worlds, users selected or created an "avatar"—a visual representation of themselves—who could then move around inside a two-dimensional or three-dimensional world under the user's control and interact with other avatars. Some of these worlds were purely experimental and noncommercial. Others were operated as commercial ventures. The largest of these virtual worlds, Fujitsu's WorldsAway, attracted 100,000 users at its peak in 1999. The richness of experience that these worlds could offer was limited, however, by the state of computer technology and the relatively slow dial-up connections that were the norm at the time.

Eventually, almost all of these worlds disappeared. With the introduction of more powerful computers and the widespread availability of high-speed broadband connections, however, a new generation of more sophisticated virtual worlds has appeared in the past few years.

Unlike Wikipedia, Second Life is a for-profit business. Linden Lab makes money by selling virtual "land" in its virtual world to "residents." The company charges users a monthly fee to control a certain amount of land, and it provides tools that allow them to build all sorts of structures on that land. Users also have the ability to create an almost unlimited variety of other virtual objects—clothing, jewelry, art works—

which they own and can buy and sell, using Linden dollars ($L), Second Life's virtual currency. (Subscribers receive a certain amount of Linden dollars based on their usage; they can amass more money through their online transactions.)

Second Life has developed a vibrant economy that is based on hundreds of thousands of monthly transactions among its users. Linden dollars also are convertible into U.S. dollars on a public exchange. The Second Life avatar featured on the cover of *Business Week*, Anshe Chung (in real life, a Chinese-born language instructor living in Germany), operates a virtual real estate development business inside Second Life that has 10 full-time employees in Wuhan, China. Another participant, Australian Nathan Keir, created a game in Second Life called Tringo that proved to be so popular that he has licensed it to a game publisher that plans to release a version for video game players.[12] However, much of Second Life's user-created content is given away, not sold. According to Linden Lab's Cory Ondrejka, approximately 40 percent of all content in Second Life can be copied freely.

As Second Life has grown, it has attracted the attention of many real-world companies and institutions. Among the corporations that are experimenting with promoting their brands inside Second Life are Adidas/Reebok, MTV, Sony, Sun Microsystems, Starwood Hotels, Toyota, and Wells Fargo. Clothing manufacturer American Apparel has set up a store in Second Life, where it sells virtual clothes. Nissan has launched a promotion that allows avatars to drive virtual cars in the virtual world.[13] IBM purchased 10 islands in Second Life to provide a new means for its globally distributed workforce to meet and share ideas. IBM also reached agreements with Sears and Circuit City to build virtual stores for them in Second Life. In a move that demonstrates that traditional media have taken notice of this trend, Reuters established a news bureau inside Second Life and assigned a full-time reporter to cover events in Second Life.[14]

craigslist

Somewhere between the nonprofit Wikipedia and the for-profit Second Life is the nominally commercial craigslist, which is defined by Wikipedia as "a centralized network of online urban communities, featuring free classified advertisements (with jobs, housing, personals, for sale/barter/wanted, services, community, gigs, and resumes categories) and forums sorted by various topics."

The site originally was established in San Francisco in 1995 by Craig Newmark, who set it up to provide a convenient way for friends to let others know when and where parties and other interesting events were being held. The site is now the most popular resource in the San Francisco Bay area for finding housing or jobs and for buying and selling all sorts of goods. The power of craigslist comes from its highly efficient organization and the ability of a user to search the site's extensive listings to find just what he or she is looking for.

As of mid-2006, craigslist had expanded from San Francisco (which is still the most active location) to more than 300 cities worldwide. It attracts more than 15 million visitors each month and generates more than five billion page views, and it undoubtedly is responsible for generating millions of dollars in commerce among its users. However, craigslist has successfully resisted all temptations to become slicker or more commercial. With its slightly funky, lowercase-text-only home page, the site remains visually simple and unadorned. The entire global enterprise is operated with a staff of slightly more than 20 people who work out of an old house in a largely residential San Francisco neighborhood. The company's only revenue comes from charges for help-wanted job ads in San Francisco, Los Angeles, and New York City and apartment listings in New York City.

In addition to paying the company's operating expenses, revenues go to a private foundation that supports emerging nonprofit organizations. Although Newmark remains actively engaged in the operation of craigslist, in 2000 he hired a CEO to run the company. Newmark's current title is "founder and customer service representative," which accurately describes the role he plays in maintaining the site on a daily basis. His abiding concern is not simply to see that the site operates smoothly but to ensure that it stays true to the spirit of community that it was originally designed to serve. In this sense, Newmark is spiritually closer to Dorothy Day of Hull House than to Jeff Bezos of Amazon.com or Bill Gates of Microsoft.

Ironically, as modest and minimally commercial as craigslist may be, it probably poses the greatest economic threat to traditional newspapers because it competes directly with newspapers' classified ad business. An

August 2006 article in *The Economist* titled "Who Killed the Newspaper?" quotes Rupert Murdoch as describing classified ads as the newspaper industry's "rivers of gold." Murdoch also notes, however, that "sometimes rivers dry up."[15] Just as Wikipedia has been able to largely match the quality of existing encyclopedias and add additional capabilities while giving its content away, craigslist and other Internet sites have provided a better and cheaper alternative to newspapers' classified ads.[16]

Enter the Blogs

The most extreme manifestation of the desire of Internet users to be producers of their own content instead of (or as well as) consumers of content may be the burgeoning world of blogs. According to a survey by the Pew Internet and American Life Project, 12 million Americans—or roughly 4 percent of the entire U.S. population—now maintain a blog.[17] Blogs appear to be even more popular in Japan than in this country: According to Peter Hirshberg of Technorati, 41 percent of all blogs are in Japanese, compared to 26 percent in English.

Hirshberg acknowledged that he was initially skeptical that "stuff created by ordinary people could be any good." He now believes that content that is being produced "by the audience talking to itself" is beginning to surpass traditional media in some areas. For example, he asserted that better information about parenting is now available from online "mommy sites" than from traditional magazines.

Because blogs are so easy to create and the cost of publishing a blog is so low, the Internet clearly has made a broader range of content available. Many blogs are simply vehicles for the expression of individual opinion. In some cases, people with specialized knowledge or specific passions—professional or personal—blog about the things that interest them. Whether this content is interesting to others depends, in part, on whether the bloggers are knowledgeable and articulate, as well as the degree to which others happen to share a blogger's interests or passions.

According to the Pew survey, about one-third of bloggers consider themselves to be engaged in a form of journalism. To blogging's most ardent supporters, this rapidly growing army of "citizen journalists" is posing a direct challenge to the gatekeepers of traditional news media. The positive contribution of blogs has been demonstrated most clearly during sudden disasters such as the December 2005 Asian tsunami, Hurricane Katrina, and the July 2005 London subway bombing: Ordinary individuals have been able to report on what they have seen and experienced more quickly and directly than reporters from traditional media have.

To critics, the actual journalistic accomplishments of bloggers have yet to live up to the ambitious claims for their importance. In a critique of citizen journalists in *The New Yorker* tellingly titled "Amateur Hour," Nicholas Lehman argues:

> **One-third of bloggers consider themselves to be engaged in a form of journalism.**
>
> *Pew Internet and American Life Project*

> Even at its best and most ambitious, citizen journalism reads like a decent Op-Ed page, and not one that offers daring, brilliant, forbidden opinions that would otherwise be unavailable. Most citizen journalism reaches very small and specialized audiences and is proudly minor in its concerns.[18]

Daniel Schorr, the veteran reporter and senior news analyst on National Public Radio (NPR), admitted that he found himself "alternately fascinated and appalled" by the new media that are challenging many of the principles of professional journalism he was trained to hold dear. Joseph Nye, distinguished service professor at the John F. Kennedy School of Government at Harvard, said that he was willing to grant that user-generated content that proliferates on the Internet is well suited to "harness the wisdom of the crowds." In a world of "too much content," however, Nye said that he believes traditional media are still needed to provide reliable expert opinion. Kwaku Sakyi-Addo, a Ghana-based broadcaster for the BBC World Service, added that as a journalist he is interested in the views of experts, but he also wants to be able to hear "the voice of the people." Neither can be substituted for the other.

As content on the Internet continues to proliferate, users are becoming more discriminating about what online information they are willing to trust. The USC Internet survey found that although many users are willing to trust online information posted by established media or the government, they are more skeptical about information posted by individuals. In 2005, 78.5 percent of users said that they trust that information on the Web sites of established media (such as nytimes.com or cnn.com) is reliable and accurate, whereas just 11.5 percent trusted information posted by individuals to be reliable and accurate.

New Options for Adding Value

In this rich but anarchic environment, an important challenge for old and new media alike is to help users navigate through the immense sea of online content to find information that is reliable and of interest to them. Arthur Sulzberger of *The New York Times* explained that one of the roles that his newspaper is taking on is to "edit the Web"—or, perhaps more accurately, to "curate the Web" for its readers. The newspaper's Web site will carry blogs by its own staff and provide a listing of top blogs on a given topic.

The mission of Technorati, according to Peter Hirshberg, also is to provide "meta-torial" content that helps users access and make use of the immense body of content being created by bloggers. Technorati does this not just by providing search capabilities but also by aggregating online discussions in a way that makes them useful and understandable. The site's home page has been redesigned to make it look more like a newspaper, organizing content from the "blogosphere" by categories and providing a convenient overview of the most popular topics currently being discussed by bloggers.

New Metrics

In this new world of wikis and blogs, new metrics may be needed to establish credibility and trust. Lance Conn, executive vice president of Vulcan, Inc., pointed out that we are still in the early days of this new way to communicate and therefore are still ironing out many of the kinks in the process. One of the key challenges is to develop new mechanisms for establishing trust. For many people, the fallback is to rely on established brands. In this new world, the challenge to these brands is to be sufficiently transparent about how they operate.

For example, although what bloggers do may be related to journalism, blogging also has some unique characteristics. According to Shel Israel, a prominent blogger and co-author (with Robert Scoble) of

Naked Conversations, what bloggers are doing is not simply expressing their own views but participating in an "ongoing conversation" within the blogosphere. In practical terms, effective bloggers pay attention to and respond to what other bloggers are saying. From this perspective, blogging is a form of what Israel calls social media. David Carr, writing in *The New York Times*, expresses the difference between traditional media and blogs even more succinctly: "Blogs, which may look like one more way to publish, are first and foremost a way to listen."[19]

> **Blogs are first and foremost a way to listen.**
>
> *David Carr*

Digg, which describes itself as a "user-driven social content website," is another approach to helping users to find worthwhile information online. The site provides users with an easy way to identify online content they like and believe would be of interest to others. This content then is listed on the Digg Web site, where other members of the "Digg community" can vote for it. Stories that get the highest number of votes are displayed most prominently on the site. What is popular on Digg is not always particularly momentous or even serious. The top-ranked stories tend to be about either celebrities in the news or obscure but interesting aspects of technology.

Digg's ranking system has generated some controversy. When one blogger analyzed the top entries on Digg, he concluded that small groups of members may be manipulating the system to generate artificially high rankings for certain stories.[20] Whether this problem is simply an example of growing pains for a new system or a fatal flaw remains to be seen.

Tracy Westen, CEO of the Center for Governmental Studies, suggested that the nature of creativity itself—or at least the way we understand creativity—may be changing. We are most familiar with the sort of individual creativity of artists and others that typically requires some degree of isolation. There also may be a kind of "social creativity," however, that is being fostered by the collaborative tools provided by the Internet. Similarly, academics and other intellectuals typically are committed to analytic processes that may take years to reach fruition. In the online world, however, there is a pressure for instant analysis and conclusions that can be boiled down to a concise soundbite. It may be too soon to know whether these new possibilities add to the useful sum of knowledge and lead to a more enlightened society. In the meantime, Westen concluded, "we are experimenting with ourselves."

NPR's Daniel Schorr suggested, not entirely facetiously, that the emergence of the new user-centered media may be something like Alfred Nobel's invention of dynamite—an innovation that is capable of being used for constructive purposes (such as mining and road building) but also has considerable potential for mayhem and destruction. Schorr concluded that we need to pay attention to the "social threats as well as the social potential" of the new media.

The Attention Economy: Marketing to the Next Generation and the Power of Choice

The relationship of consumers to technology has shifted in fundamental ways, according to Ted Cohen, managing partner of Tag Strategic. Thanks to a variety of new technologies, the "physics of the media world" are changing—from a world in which attention was abundant and content was scarce to a world in which content is superabundant and attention is scarce. With so many competing options, the individual's attention is now the most valuable commodity.

In the past, new technologies evoked a sense of wonderment—a sense of "Wow!" from consumers about what technology could do. Eventually that response faded, and consumers began to feel empowered by what technology allowed them to do. Today we have reached a new stage in which the main feeling among consumers is one of entitlement. Consumers now say, "I want choices, I want them now, and don't try to tell me how to get what I want."

This shift has been brought about through an array of technologies that expand choice by acting as *time shifters* (e.g., digital video recorders such as TiVo), *place shifters* (such as Slingbox, a device that links a home television through the Internet to a personal computer that can be located anywhere), *connectors* (e.g., Skype, which provides free voice connections globally over the Internet), *filters and recommenders* (e.g., Google, Technorati, and Digg), and a plethora of hardware devices for accessing and viewing content (e.g., personal computers, televisions, personal digital assistants [PDAs], mobile phones, MP3 players, DVD players, and video game players).

In this world of ever-expanding choices, "quality" of content is no longer the critical factor in determining success. What matters most now is relevance. What users choose to spend time watching, listening to, or reading is not necessarily what is "best" or what is most heavily marketed to them; it is what appeals most to them. A good example is Google's "Top 100 Videos." This listing of popular video clips online consists mostly of anonymous or amateur material that is funny or offbeat but rarely reflects high production values.

Quality of content is no longer the critical factor in success. What matters most now is relevance.

What marketers in this new world need to know is how people find out about what is available and how they make choices about what they find appealing. Lynda Resnick of Roll International noted that "the whole paradigm of marketing has changed" as a result of the new media environment. For example, Resnick's company now allocates a "huge part" of its advertising budget to purchasing keywords on search engines such as Google (see "Google's Ad-Words," page 19). According to Resnick, most ad agencies have yet to recognize and embrace the new media. She believes, however, that a good marketer should be able to market a product effectively in this new media environment for one-tenth the budget that such marketing required previously. Jordan Greenhall, CEO of DivX, noted that his company was able to grow to reach an audience of 180 million users on a marketing budget of zero by using the Internet's viral marketing capabilities.

The Paradox of Choice

Former U.S. Secretary of State Madeleine Albright recalled her experience in escorting a group of Czech citizens around the United States after that country's "velvet revolution." One of their stops was a typical U.S. supermarket. Albright's Czech visitors initially were amazed by the proliferation of choices available to U.S. consumers, including 25 different types of mustard. After a while, however, they began to ask, "Why does anyone need 25 different kinds of mustard?" The Internet seems to provide the opportunity to have thousands of different choices for a single product category. How users are responding to this new abundance of choice is another facet of the evolution of the Internet.

In his book *The Long Tail*, Chris Anderson argues that the expansion of choice made possible by the Internet has brought about a significant and unexpected shift in consumer buying behavior. The distribution economics of traditional physical media such as movies, records, CDs, and books have driven those businesses to be dominated by big hits and made it increasingly difficult for works that attract a smaller audience to survive. (This dichotomy was summed up by best-selling author James Michener, who was asked by an aspiring writer if it is possible to make a living through writing. Michener replied that "you can make a killing as a writer, but you can't make a living.") In the digital world, however, things are different. The cost of maintaining inventory is far lower than in the physical world, and the reach of the Internet is so great that even obscure works can find an audience. The result is that an online store that sells CDs, movies, or books can generate substantial sales from virtually its entire catalog—the "misses" as well as the "hits."

Online communities are powerful concentrators of information.

How do consumers find the content they want, however, in a world of virtually unlimited choice? Too much choice can be paralyzing. In fact, there is evidence that when people are presented with more than a handful of choices, they tend to lose interest.[21] Few people, if any, are interested in browsing through a store with 100,000 choices.

The challenge is to cut through the clutter of irrelevant choices and provide access to the particular alternatives that are of interest to a particular consumer. Good search tools are part of the answer. Another element is traditional mass media advertising, which continues to play a role in creating awareness of products, which then motivates consumers to seek more information online. Chris Sacca, head of special initiatives for Google, noted that whereas the television and the personal computer have been in separate rooms in most U.S. households, that has begun to change in the past few years. With the spread of WiFi networks and the increasing popularity of laptops, televisions and personal computers have moved into the same space, and users often are using both together. We now live in a world in which multitasking is the norm, especially for younger people, who operate in what Peter Hirshberg described as a state of "continuous partial attention."

Google has been able to document the interaction of the new and old media in its search statistics: It has found a strong relationship between specific televised ads and a spike in searches on the topic of the ad. The relationship between online and offline behavior operates in both directions, however. An analysis of Google search topics found that there was a high degree of correlation between the popularity of searches on the titles of theatrical movies before their release and the success of those films at the box office. The research showed that the number of searches on a movie title during the week before the film's release was 86 percent accurate in predicting ticket sales on its opening weekend. The number of searches six weeks before the film's opening was 82 percent accurate in predicting its performance at the box office. The analysis found a similar correlation for new music releases.

Deven Parekh, managing director of Insight Partner Ventures, described another approach to aggregating demand for niche products. Netshops is a collection of online specialty shops, each of which provides access to an extensive selection of products within a single, narrowly defined category such as dartboards, barstools, water fountains, or rocking chairs. Each shop has its own identity, but all of the shops share a common "back end" with other shops for order processing and fulfillment.

The most influential source of information about products and services, however, comes, as always, from word of mouth: recommendations from trusted sources-friends, family members, or acknowledged experts. Online communities made up of people with common interests are powerful concentrators of this kind of information. Individual travelers who are willing to share their personal experiences with airlines, hotels, and so forth are likely to be more trusted and have greater influence than professional travel agents. Research has shown that people today are less likely to trust institutions and more likely to trust "people like me." [22]

Building Trust

How does one decide who is trustworthy in the online world? The key, according to John Clippinger, senior fellow at the Berkman Center for Internet and Society at Harvard Law School, is to develop "reputation systems" that can be used to establish trust. According to an analysis by researchers at the University of Michigan School of Information, such systems are vital in an Internet environment in which strangers want to do business with each other:

> When you interact with someone over time, the history of past interactions informs you about the other party's abilities and disposition. You learn when you can count on that party, [and] the expectation of reciprocity or retaliation in future interaction creates an incentive for good behavior. Robert Axelrod refers to this as the "shadow of the future," an expectation that people will consider each other's past in future interactions. That shadow constrains behavior in the present.
>
> Between strangers, on the other hand, trust is much harder to build, and understandably so. Strangers do not have known past histories or the prospect of future interactions, and they are not subject to a network of informed individuals who will punish bad and reward good behavior toward any of them. In some sense, a stranger's good name is not at stake. Given these factors, the temptation to "hit and run" outweighs the incentive to cooperate, since the future casts no shadow.... Reputation systems seek to restore the shadow of the future to each transaction by creating an expectation that other people will look back upon it.[23]

One important element of eBay's success has been its feedback system, which uses input from users who have done business with buyers and sellers to rate them on their reliability. Buyers and sellers know that they will be rated on every transaction and recognize the importance of maintaining a positive reputation. Hence, sellers are motivated to describe accurately the items they are selling and send them promptly to purchasers, and buyers are motivated to pay punctually for items they purchase. The key to the power of the system is the element of reciprocity.

Zoë Baird, president of the John and Mary R. Markle Foundation, pointed out that one way trust traditionally has been created in the marketplace has been though laws that establish a clear framework for commerce. As new tools for building trust online are being developed, however, there may be less need for legal protections.   Another area where legal action has been regarded as necessary is in protecting individuals against the excessive power of monopolies.   This protection has been important, for example, in telecommunications and broadcasting—industries in which relatively few, very large players have dominated. Is concern about monopoly power still relevant given the proliferation of communication channels online and the ability of individuals to express themselves on an equal footing with traditional media?   Clay T. Whitehead, distinguished visiting professor of communication policy at George Mason University, expanded on this point by noting that he had spent many years working to break down monopoly structures in telecommunications and the media, but now much of this structure appears to have been "blown away" by competition in infrastructure and the new media. There may be less need now for government regulation, particularly content regulation, than in the past. Net-based trust systems may be more effective protectors of the public interest than traditional government regulators. As Federal Communications Commission (FCC) Commissioner Robert McDowell asked, do questions of media ownership still matter, or are we trying to put a ball and chain on a dinosaur?

Global Consequences of Next-Generation Media

New communications technologies are creating a new environment internationally as well as in the United States. The world is rapidly getting wired, and the Internet is spreading around the globe. Yet the largest technological impact globally is coming not from the Internet but from the mobile phone.

The largest technological impact globally is coming from the mobile phone.

There are already more than 2 billion mobile phones in use globally, and according to the consulting firm Market Intelligence, the number of mobile phones in the world will exceed 2.5 billion before the end of 2006—more than twice the number of land lines. More than 20 years elapsed before the first billion mobile phones were in service; just four years were needed to reach the second billion. At the current pace the third billion—the point at which mobile phone penetration will have reached nearly half the world's population—will be in service in less than two years, by the end of 2007.[24]

Remarkably, mobile phone penetration already exceeds 100 percent in 30 countries (i.e., there are more mobile phones than people), including Hong Kong where penetration reached 126.5 percent as of May 2005,[25] Taiwan, Italy, the United Kingdom, Sweden, and Finland (see Figure 2). China has by far the largest number of mobile phones in service—400 million—compared to about 200 million in the United States, the country with the second largest number of mobile phones. Moreover, China is adding nearly five million new subscribers each month.

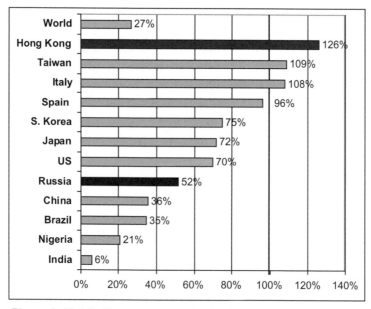

Figure 2: Mobile Phone Penetration in Selected Countries, 2005
Source: CIA World Factbook, 2006

While the number of mobile phones in use continues to rise, their capabilities also continue to improve. For many users globally, sending and receiving text messages is as important as or more important than talking on a mobile phone. Many newer handsets offer features such as games, music players, cameras, and geopositioning (the ability to determine the phone's location). "Smart phones" that include many capabilities of computers are becoming more common as they become less expensive. In Europe and other parts of the world, so-called Third Generation (3G) networks are now operating; these networks support delivery of full-motion video as well as text and voice. Television producers have already begun to create video content that has been developed specifically for delivery to cell phones.

Mobile phones have become deeply embedded in the lives of many users. According to a survey of young adults, ages 15 to 35, in 11 countries—including the United Kingdom, Spain, Brazil, China, India, Saudi Arabia, and the United States—conducted in 2006 for Nokia, a majority of mobile phone users "cannot imagine life without their mobile phone." One-fifth of young mobile phone users said that they would be more upset at losing their mobile phone than losing their wallet, their credit cards, or their wedding ring. Nearly three-quarters (72 percent) reported that they no longer use an alarm clock in the morning; instead, they depend on the alarm in their mobile phone to wake them. Among respondents who were not currently using a mobile phone, 94 percent said that they planned to get one.[26]

> **Mobile phone penetration will have reached nearly half the world's population by the end of 2007.**

The most dramatic impact of the mobile phone is being felt in the developing world. Although penetration in Africa is only about 20 percent of the population, the growth of new mobile customers is very high: Over the past 12 months, the growth rate was nearly 100 percent—approximately twice the world rate of 50 percent.[27] In Ghana more than one-third of the population now has mobile phones, compared to just 3 percent with Internet access. Nigeria is now one of the 10 fastest-growing mobile phone markets in the world.

In much of the developing world, cell phones are not supplementing or replacing land lines; they are bringing phone service to these communities for the first time.[28] To illustrate the impact that the introduction of mobile phones has had in places such as Africa, Kwaku Sakyi-Addo of BBC World told a story about getting his father a mobile phone for his 80th birthday. Although his father had worked as an education officer in Ghana when he was younger, he rarely had access to any phone service. Sakyi-Addo explained what happened after his father, who lives in a village about an hour from the capital, got the phone:

> He asked my cousin, a teacher, who lives in the town to come over and show him what to do with it. It wasn't long before he called me to say thank you. But it was few days later before he managed to send his first text message. "This is your dad. Are you receiving this message?" the text asked.
>
> "Yes, yes, Dad," I texted back excitedly.
>
> "Thank you for this," he keyed back.
>
> "U R welcome, Dad," I replied.
>
> Then I received yet another text shortly afterward, this time from my cousin: "Ur father is crying."
>
> "Me 2," I replied.

Mobile phones also are being used to extend the reach of traditional media. During recent elections in Ghana, individual "citizen journalists" used their phones to call in reports of local results to radio stations that broadcast the information nationally.

Funmi Iyanda, host of "New Dawn with Funmi," a popular national television program in Nigeria, agreed that mobile phones are a powerful tool. Iyanda personally pays for eight cell phones so that members of her family can be connected. She noted that in much of Africa, broadcast media, including television and radio, still have the broadest reach and remain highly influential. Increasingly, however, Africans are putting more trust into what they hear directly from others through these new media.

For much of the world, a mobile phone rather than a personal computer is likely to be the principal access device to the Internet. Yet as FOCAS co-chair and former FCC Chairman Reed Hundt noted, mobile phone networks are not open in the same way the Internet is. Cell phone networks are entirely owned and controlled by their operators.

Anyone who wants to use one of the wireless networks to distribute content can do so only with the permission of its operator. In some countries, governments maintain control over cell phone networks and regard them as a potential threat to their authority. Hundt noted that it would be helpful if the United States took a strong position in favor of open cell phone networks.

Wiring the World

These new media—the Internet and the mobile phone—are helping to create a new global political dynamic. The best way to understand this shift, according to John Rendon of the Rendon Group, is to look at "self-organizing systems" that are not structured hierarchically but are able to function effectively. A simple example is the way a colony of ants operates. Wikipedia, which is being created and maintained by thousands of individual, independent contributors who share a few common guiding principles, is another example. The impact of bloggers, who are even more loosely connected but keep in contact with what other bloggers with common interests are saying, is yet another example.

The result is that we are no longer living in a single political "universe" but in a radically decentralized "multiverse." Although this new world may be unfamiliar, Rendon argued that it is in the strategic interest of the United States that the world get wired. Having a robust communications infrastructure that lets people talk with one another may be a prerequisite for breaking the power of elite autocracies and converting authoritarian governments to democracies. According to Joseph Nye of the Kennedy School of Government at Harvard, 30,000 police in China are attempting to monitor more than 100 million Internet users and 400 million cell phone users. These new media cannot be controlled, and they are helping to bring about a social and sexual revolution that will provide the basis for the demand for political change.

Creating better connections between Americans and people abroad is critical to improving the standing of this country in the world. John Rendon cited a study of attitudes toward the United States among people in other countries that found that those who had had direct contact with Americans, either by studying or working in the United States, or had immediate family members who did so, tended to define this country in terms of the American people. Their opinion of the United States ranged from highly positive to mildly negative. Those who had not had any direct contact with Americans, however, typically regard this country in terms of U.S. companies and had more negative attitudes. Those who were separated by an even greater degree tended to view the United States in terms of the country's foreign policy and had the most negative attitudes of all.[29]

In the long run, Rendon argued, engagement in communication with the rest of the world, by the American people, not just their government, is in the strategic interest of this country. The government should not be the primary actor, but it should be the enabler of this kind of communication.

According to several FOCAS participants, the U.S. government has failed to recognize this shift and continues to use an outmoded top-down model for communicating with the world. Nye noted that the U.S. government currently spends $500 million annually on "public diplomacy" that is intended to explain and defend our policies to the rest of the world. About $100 million of this money goes to support Alhurra, the federally funded Arab-language satellite television service. The service was launched in 2004 as the "U.S. answer to Al-Jazeera." The network's programs are slick and have high production values, but they are widely viewed by the intended audience as U.S. propaganda. By contrast, the United States spends about $30 million on Radio Sawa, a service that is aimed at younger people in Arabic countries. The content of Radio Sawa is mainly pop music programs. As a result, its programming is considerably more popular in the Middle East than that of Alhurra.

In fact, according to Nye—who coined the concept of "soft power" in his 1990 book *Bound to Lead*—the United States has been most effective in the world when it has used a combination of soft power and hard power. The Berlin Wall was brought down by sledgehammers wielded by the citizens of Germany who demanded freedom for themselves, not by bombs or military action. A more effective use of television to communicate U.S. values would be to turn Alhurra into an international version of C-SPAN, supporting citizen-to-citizen communication from this country's civil society, rather than acting as a megaphone for official government positions.

Former Secretary of State Madeleine Albright agreed that the approach this country has taken in communicating with the world is not true public diplomacy. We are engaged not in a "clash of civilizations" but in a battle of ideas with our adversaries. Our messages are being discounted and ignored because they are regarded as a "control mechanism," not a good-faith effort to engage in dialogue, which involves listening as well as speaking. We should be expanding exchanges with foreign students, yet we are closing the doors to immigration in the name of national security. Although Albright believes in the concept of soft power, she worries that the label is counterproductive: "The problem with soft power is that it sounds soft."

Supporting greater interconnectedness among everyone may be in our long-term interest, but it also has a dark side. People tend to listen to the ideas that are appealing to them, and the Internet allows everyone to find reinforcement for their own point of view. As Arthur Sulzberger of *The New York Times* asked, "If being wired is so positive, why is there such a rapid growth of militant fundamentalism around the world? If Afghanistan were totally wired, would terrorist cells stop growing?" Certainly the Internet helps niche groups of all types coalesce. As David Ignatius noted in a column in *The Washington Post*, quoting Charles McLean, the Internet can act as a "rage enabler," providing "instant, persistent, real-time stimuli [that] takes anger to a higher level."[30]

Moreover, extremists also are using the latest technologies, such as video games and wikis, as recruitment tools. As Cory Ondrejka of Linden Lab noted, we may be the only ones who are not using these tools to communicate with the rest of the world. Although hearing someone express a viewpoint that agrees with one's own may be gratifying, engaging in constructive collaboration with others helps to build trust. For example, the popularity of Wikipedia is global. There are already Wikipedia entries in more than 150 languages, and there are more than 20,000 entries each in 30 different languages. Although the spread of technology will have disparate effects, not all of which are benign, its overall impact is likely to favor greater democratization, particularly if we can help to shape its evolution.

Not every development in the world can be explained by technology, but technology matters—and so does the content that is being disseminated by it. Tracy Westen concluded the discussion by noting that in the 20th century more than 100 million deaths were caused by "toxic ideologies." Just as we have developed effective means of counteracting physical toxins, we need to find methods for combating pernicious ideas and ideologies. We need to come up with new narratives that will be credible to the world and effectively convey our values and beliefs. Moreover, rather than relying on official government spokespeople, the best way to do this may be to trust the American people themselves, empowered by technology, to tell their own stories and develop their own links with the rest of the world.

Citizenship for the Next Generation

The impact of the Internet has continued to spread to more aspects of society, including government. Virtually every elected official in the United States now has a Web site and is able to receive e-mail communications from constituents. Many routine government functions, such as obtaining licenses or paying taxes, can now be conducted online. There is no doubt that the intense scrutiny paid to politics and politicians by bloggers has had a real impact on the political process.

Has technology made democracies more democratic? To explore this question, the FOCAS participants debated a hypothetical "modest proposal" from Tracy Westen of the Center for Governmental Studies for "Open Source Democracy for the Digital Age" (see sidebar for proposal text). Framed as an amendment to the California constitution, the proposal from the (fictional) California Digital Coalition would expand that state's current citizen initiative process to permit California voters "to create, circulate, qualify, and vote for ballot initiatives—all online." The basic premise of the proposal is that we now have tools that will allow us to move closer to the ideal of participatory democracy. As Westen put it, "If everything else is going online, it makes sense for government to be online as well." He also pointed out that trust in government has been declining, and numerous polls have shown that voters want to be more involved in the political process.

A MODEST PROPOSAL:
OPEN SOURCE DEMOCRACY FOR THE DIGITAL AGE

Proposed Constitutional Amendment by the California Digital Coalition (CDC)

Preamble: California has already pioneered a new hybrid form of democracy. Voters enact policies directly through ballot initiatives (direct democracy) and indirectly through elected representatives (indirect democracy) who enact legislation. However, the failures of representative democracy (campaign finance abuses, gerrymandering, public distrust, low voter turnout) and the explosive growth of digital communication require a reshaping of California's basic democratic institutions. In the spirit of 21st Century Founding Fathers and Mothers, **CDC proposes that California voters be able to create, circulate, qualify, and vote for ballot initiatives—all online.** This will increase citizen participation in democratic institutions and create new checks and balances for the digital age.

1. **Online Digital Signatures:** By 2008, the Secretary of State shall issue all registered voters a free personal encrypted digital signature to use online to register to vote, sign ballot initiative petitions, and vote in elections.

2. **Wiki Website:** By 2010, the Secretary of State shall create a website with wiki software and allow proponents of any new ballot initiative to post the draft text of that measure on the website for at least 90 days. Members of the public shall be able to submit amendments to that text; proponents will have the power to accept or reject amendments. (Dissatisfied participants can create their own initiatives.)

3. **Initiative Qualification:** When a proponent has finished accepting amendments, he may post the final text on the state website for 90 days. If he gathers 500,000 online digital signatures, the measure will appear on the next statewide ballot. Proponents must disclose their top three largest campaign contributors. Signers must cycle through pro and con arguments before signing.

4. **Option for Legislative Negotiation:** Once the initiative has qualified for the ballot, the legislature has 30 days to adopt substitute legislation. If proponent believes the substitute legislation adequately implements the principal objectives of his proposed initiative, he may withdraw the initiative from the ballot. Otherwise, proponent may place the initiative on the statewide ballot.

5. **Online Voting:** All citizens may vote at a ballot box, by absentee ballot, or by online digital signature. After 2016, all voting shall be via online digital signature within 30 days of a measure qualifying for the ballot.

6. **Online Amendments:** At least five years after adoption of an initiative, any citizen can propose an amendment. Amendments must be subject to comment on the state's wiki website. If the legislature approves any amendments by a two-thirds vote, they will become law, providing they are consistent with the purposes and intent of the original initiative.

Westen's proposal was intentionally provocative. His aim was to stimulate a meaningful debate on what measures should be taken, if any, to anticipate the logical future interaction of network technologies and the electoral process.

The proposal would require California's Secretary of State to provide every registered voter with a "free personal encrypted signature" that would provide each voter with a secure verifiable identity that would allow them to sign initiative petitions and vote online. The proposal also would require the Secretary of State to create a wiki on the Internet that would permit citizens to post drafts of proposed initiatives and allow others to suggest amendments. The proponents of an initiative would have 90 days to gather—online—the signatures needed to qualify the initiative for a ballot. After a suitable period for consideration, the initiative would be voted on. By 2016, all voting would take place online 30 days after a measure has qualified for the ballot.

Not surprisingly, FOCAS participants raised many questions about the feasibility and likely effects of the proposal. Among the questions raised were the following:

- How trustworthy are digital signatures? There has already been considerable controversy regarding the reliability of electronic voting procedures. These concerns probably would be even greater if the entire political process were moved online.

  On the other hand, we now rely on documents such as driver's licenses to establish identity, even though we know that they can be counterfeited. If a digital signature is as reliable as a driver's license, it probably is good enough for this purpose.

- Is the current technology ready to support this kind of activity? For example, is wiki software really the right tool for this process? Although wikis have been used successfully for a wide variety of collaborative projects, and Wikipedia has shown that thousands of individuals can work together to create a valuable resource, what has been at stake in such projects is considerably lower than what would be at stake for elections. We do not know if wiki software is capable of supporting millions of individuals who might participate in this online process. (There are approximately 16 million registered voters in California.) Yet if a particular technology has been embedded in a constitutional amendment, we would be stuck with it.

- Even if technology is not a problem, will this proposal enhance democracy or diminish it? By lowering the barrier to participation even further—citizens would be able to vote without ever having to leave home—this proposal could actually erode true citizen involvement in politics. Particularly if initiatives can be submitted, qualified for the ballot, and voted on at any time, the political process could become a nearly continuous activity. How many people will have enough commitment to remain actively involved in such a process on an ongoing basis? Special interest groups that would have the incentive to put in the time and energy required to remain engaged could effectively capture the process for their own narrow purposes.

As Peter Hirshberg of Technorati observed, "Electronic democracy should be more about democracy and less about electronic." In designing any online system, we need to be sure that it will actually broaden participation, not narrow it further.

- Finally, even if the proposed process worked as advertised, is it a wise idea? After all, at the founding of this country, our Founding Fathers had a debate about how we should govern ourselves. Thomas Jefferson argued that the people should govern themselves as much as possible, whereas Alexander Hamilton argued that government should be made up of the best representatives of the people, chosen democratically. We chose a representative democracy then, and most Americans seem to approve of that system. Simply because new technologies allow us to change the means of governance does not mean we ought to abandon a political system that has served us well for several centuries.

This concern was expressed most strongly by former FCC Chairman Reed Hundt, who argued that elected representatives are ultimately accountable for their legislative votes. If we allow voters to pass any laws, however, then no one can be held accountable for the consequences. Laws will be passed by voters who are anonymous and unaccountable. Moreover, many issues that politicians grapple with are complicated and require real deliberation. Technology tends to shorten the timeframe for deliberation, and this proposal would encourage simplistic proposals to be offered and decided on, with little or no real deliberation. As FCC Commissioner Robert McDowell warned, there is a danger that decisions will be driven by voters' passions of the moment, with little regard for nuances or the long-term consequences of their actions.

- A related concern is whether moving a key component of the political process online would inevitably favor voters who are tech savvy and disenfranchise those who are less technically astute. There has been considerable debate about the extent of the "digital divide" between the wired and unwired, but there clearly is a relationship between the likelihood of being online and factors such as income and level of education. Until everyone is online, proposals such as this will reinforce the power of elites.

To address concerns about the reliability of online voting, Jeff Cole of the Center for the Digital Future at USC's Annenberg School for Communication pointed out that e-voting is already in place in Estonia. That country's Parliament passed a law in 2002 authorizing online voting, which was used for the first time in municipal elections in 2005. The law required that e-voting "offer the same level of security and confidence as traditional voting," which has meant instituting an elaborate series of safeguards to authenticate voters' identities and ensure the integrity of their votes. To vote online, Estonians must use electronic identification cards ("smart cards")—which already are in use by more than 85 percent of registered voters—as well as a personal identification number (PIN) and a device that is attached to the computer used for voting to read the electronic ID. The voters' choices are encrypted, and voters use their "digital signature" to reconfirm their identify before their ballot is sent to Estonia's National Electoral Committee for counting.[31]

Although FOCAS co-chair Reed Hundt agreed that using technology to strengthen democracy is a laudable goal, he argued that this proposal seemed to be going about it the wrong way. The role of government, he suggested, is "to do those things that need doing but the people can't do for themselves." By contrast, the role of technology is to increase the number of things people can do for themselves and, therefore, reduce the scope of what government needs to do. From this perspective, trying to use technology to expand the power of majorities is counterproductive; it is more likely to strengthen diverse local communities.

In reflecting on this debate, Madeleine Albright recalled some of the lessons she has learned as Chair of the National Democratic Institute (NDI), a federally chartered nonprofit organization set up to promote the concept of democracy internationally. When the NDI was founded, no one knew what the group's message should be or how to explain what the real meaning of democracy was. The NDI's founders realized that democracy is much more than elections. One vital element is the existence of a viable opposition party. Another is the availability of multiple independent sources of information. Although the Internet

One of the effects of technology is to shorten the timeframe for decisionmaking.

seems to be multiplying the sources of information, Albright said that she fears that getting unbiased information is increasingly difficult for citizens and that Americans are becoming less knowledgeable about how democracy and government actually work. She expressed some skepticism about the extent to which this kind of problem can be fixed by technology.

Yale law professor Yochai Benkler noted that democratic governments already are being challenged by the new environment created by the Internet. Modern democracies developed in a world dominated by mass media. We need to understand more about how they function in a new world in which user-generated content is flourishing. Benkler cited the example of a single blogger who raised the issue of the reliability of Diebold electronic voting machines and included some of the source code used by the machines. After protests from Diebold, the site was shut down, but other bloggers quickly picked up the story and reposted the code. Eventually, several government jurisdictions that had adopted the machines decided to demand that Diebold make changes to increase the reliability of their machines.

This example illustrates how blogs can rapidly magnify the importance of an issue that is "of intense interest to a small group of people" in a way that would have been difficult or impossible in the pre-Internet world. One of the effects of technology certainly is to shorten the time-frame for decisionmaking. Politicians who are used to a more leisurely pace of deliberation will have to adapt to this new reality if representative democracy is to remain relevant.

Leadership for the Next Generation

The final FOCAS session explored the global implications of next-generation media. These new technologies certainly have not made many of the world's most intractable problems—poverty, violence, tyranny—disappear, but they may offer new possibilities for addressing these problems.

At the same time, every technology has a dark side and can be exploited for bad purposes as well as good. As former U.S. Secretary of State Madeleine Albright noted, radio can be a powerful disseminator of information, but in Rwanda it contributed to genocide when it was used by the government to spread hatred. In *The Washington Post* column cited previously in this report, David Ignatius argued that technology can have the perverse effect in developing countries of widening the gaps between elites, who have the ability to connect with and communicate with the larger world, and the rest of the population, who are isolated by a lack of access. It is difficult to see how the Internet, by itself, can offer much hope to the 1 billion people in the world who earn less than $2 per day.

What role can or should the new technologies play in expanding freedom? Marc Nathanson, vice chairman of the NDI and FOCAS co-chair, noted that 3 billion people—nearly half of the world's population—now live in free societies. On the other hand, 1.6 billion people (18 percent of the total population) live in partly free societies, and the remaining 36 percent, 2.3 billion people, are living in societies that are not free. Among this latter group, nearly 70 percent are under the age of 25.

Nathanson posed the following questions: "Will the new world of the next generation of media isolate us or bring us together? Will we embrace our differences, or will it cause us to retreat into our own virtual xenophobic jungle?" He then proposed that a new goal be added to the eight goals set by the UN Millennium Development Project for the international community to expand human development globally (see box). The ninth goal, according to Nathanson, should be to "provide access to appropriate new technologies."

UN Millennium Development Project Goals (2000)

- Eradicate extreme poverty and hunger
- Achieve universal primary education
- Promote gender equality and empower women
- Reduce child mortality
- Improve maternal health
- Combat HIV/AIDS, malaria and other diseases
- Ensure environmental stability
- Develop a global partnership for development

Jeff Cole of the Center for the Digital Future at the USC Annenberg School noted that in the developed world just about everyone who wants to be online can be. That is not the case in much of the rest of the world, however. In Mexico, for example, Internet penetration is only 18 percent. Even if we try to "push people online," we may not make much progress. For the residents of these countries, technologies such as radio and cell phones are likely to be much more critical. Access to these technologies may be as critical for development as ensuring access to food and water.

Yale's Yochai Benkler explained that there is a growing global movement supporting "access to knowledge" as a basic right. At the core of this movement are two ideas. The first is that every component of human development is heavily affected by information and knowledge. The fundamental means for social improvement—medicine, better agricultural practices, news media, books and software—are all "knowledge-embedded tools." The second point is that the new user-centric media enable people to do more for themselves if they are given the ability to collaborate. We need to recognize that how we manage knowledge is central to development. As Craig Newmark observed, the role for people who are trying to help is to provide these tools and then get out of the way.

Kwaku Sakyi-Addo of BBC World underlined the value of these strategies by describing the conditions in his home country of Ghana, where the average per capita income is $390 per year. Although Internet access remains very limited, other technologies are having a major impact. The country also is struggling with an AIDS epidemic. Even when drugs are made available to poor Ghanians, they have to be taken on a strict schedule to be effective. To take their drugs on schedule, people must have watches and understand how to use them. Communication technologies such as mobile phones and radio are extremely important. Using these technologies, ordinary citizens in remote parts of the country can phone a call-in radio program to ask questions of government ministers.

How we manage knowledge is central to development.

Sakyi-Addo described a new initiative by Google and Technoserve to sponsor a business plan competition in Ghana. Forty winners received between $5,000 and $15,000 to start new businesses. Among the winners who appeared on Sakyi-Addo's radio program was one person who proposed to raise pigs organically and another who wanted to establish an environmentally conscious car wash.

Nigerian radio host Funmi Iyanda noted that she grew up in a very poor family in southwestern Nigeria. Books provided Iyanda with access to a different world and let her see beyond her immediate environment and aspire to do more with her life. She believes that new technology can play the same role in the lives of young people today. More than half of Nigeria's population is under age 25, and this generation wants to be on the Internet and have cell phones. Like young people anywhere, they understand the power of technology. By empowering them, technology may make it possible to "leapfrog" the past and move the country toward greater prosperity.

Iyanda explained that she intends to go to the country's universities and secondary schools to find young Nigerians who "understand the language that people like Chris Sacca, Cory Ondrejka, and Craig Newmark are speaking" and give them a platform to express themselves. She plans to recruit young people who are making creative use of technology to appear on her television show to inspire others. To encourage use of the Internet, she will ask people who want to be on television to go online and apply to be on her show. Her goal is to help young people to create their own community where new ideas and new values can be encouraged.

New Roles in a New World

Finally, the FOCAS participants returned to the question of how the rise of next-generation media has changed the role of the United States in the world. Peter Hirshberg offered another "modest proposal"— that the leaders of this country should recognize that they have the responsibility of managing "Brand America." What every good brand manager knows is that the first step in the job is to listen to a brand's customers and understand what they are thinking. Unfortunately, feedback from the world suggests that we have not been doing a very good job of managing and promoting the U.S. brand.

New Media are creating a new vision of the relationship between the individual and society.

The new technologies provide powerful means of engaging with the world and allowing others to tell us what they think. From the perspective of public diplomacy, we need to move from a top-down, one-way advertising/propaganda model of communication to a peer-to-peer model that is based on real dialogue, on listening as well as speaking. A public diplomacy strategy that looks more like Wikipedia or craigslist might be much more effective than continuing to expand the reach and wattage of Voice of America.

Former FCC Chairman and FOCAS co-chair Reed Hundt summarized these insights by asserting that the new media are creating a new vision of the relationship between the individual and society. Leadership no longer needs to come "from above"; it can emerge from the collaborative efforts of the people themselves. In the 21st century, progress may well depend on leadership from below.

Notes

1. David Bollier, *When Push Comes to Pull* (Washington, DC: Aspen Institute, 2006), 4.

2. "Fifth Study of the Internet by the Digital Future Project Finds Major New Trends in Online Use for Political Campaigns," Center for the Digital Future, December 7, 2005. Available at http://www.digitalcenter.org/pages/current_report.asp?intGlobalId=19.

3. "More Media, Less News," *The Economist* (August 26-September 1, 2006), 52.

4. Frank Ahrens, "Gannett to Change Its Papers' Approach," *Washington Post* (November 7, 2006), D1.

5. Andrew Murr, "A Winning Equation," *Newsweek* (August 7, 2006).

6. Yochai Benkler, *The Wealth of Networks: How Social Production Transforms Markets and Freedom.* (New Haven, Conn.: Yale University Press, 2006), 70. Available at http://benkler.org.

7. Ibid., 14.

8. "Popular Demand," *New York Times* (August 14, 2006), C7.

9. Jim Giles, "Internet Encyclopedias Go Head to Head," *Nature* 438 (December 15, 2005): 900-901. A list of the errors identified by the *Nature* article was posted on Wikipedia within a few days of the appearance of the article. Within one month, all of the errors had been corrected.

10. To further expand opportunities for participant creation, Linden Lab announced that it was making its software open source. In a January 2007 posting titled "Embracing the Inevitable" on the company's official blog, it announced that its client viewer software was available for downloading and modification. See http://blog.secondlife.com/2007/01/08/embracing-the-inevitable/.

11. For a more detailed description of MUDs and MOOs, see www.lambdamoo.info and Sherry Turkle, *Life on the Screen: Identity in the Age of the Internet* (New York: Simon and Schuster, 1995). In her book, Turkle describes MUDs as "objects for thinking about postmodern selves."

12. "My Virtual Life," *Business Week* (May 1, 2006).

13. Richard Siklos, "A Virtual World but Real Money," *New York Times* (October 19, 2006), C1.

14. See www.secondlife.reuters.com.

15. "Who Killed the Newspaper," *The Economist* (August 26, 2006).

16. Rapporteur Richard Adler, who lives in the San Francisco Bay area, had a personal experience that demonstrated some of the unique strengths of craigslist in creating an efficient marketplace and building a genuine sense of community. For several years, a large "fireplace insert," weighing considerably more than 100 pounds, sat unused in Adler's garage, taking up space. Because this fireplace insert was a relatively specialized item, Adler was skeptical about the efficiency of selling it through a newspaper. Because it was too heavy to ship, he didn't think it

made sense to offer it on eBay. Adler eventually posted it for sale on craigslist. Within 24 hours, a buyer showed up at the door, paid cash for the item, and hauled it away in his truck. The next day Adler got a call from the buyer. His immediate response was that the buyer was having second thoughts about his purchase and was calling to complain or ask for his money back. The buyer had called, however, to let Adler know that he had installed the insert, that it was working fine, and that his family was very happy that their home was warm again.

17. Anada Lenhart and Susannah Fox, *Bloggers: A Portrait of the Internet's New Storytellers*, Pew Internet and American Life Project, July 19, 2006.

18. Nicholas Lehman, "Amateur Hour," *The New Yorker* (August 7 & 14, 2006), 49.

19. David Carr, "A Comeback Overshadowed by a Blog," *New York Times* (September 11, 2006), C1.

20. Antone Gonsalves, "Digg Dogges by Allegations of Manipulation," *TechWeb* (September 7, 2006). Available at http://www.informationweek.com/news/showArticle.jhtml?articleID=192600648.

21. See, for example, Barry Schwartz, *The Paradox of Choice: Why More is Less* (New York: Ecco, 2004).

22. Annual Edelman Trust Barometer, 2006. Available at www.edelman.co.uk/insights/trust/Edelman%20Trust%20Barometer%202006.pdf.

23. Paul Resnick, Richard Zeckhauser, Eric Friedman, and Ko Kuwabara, "Reputation Systems: Facilitating Trust in Internet Interactions," *Communications of the ACM* 43, no. 12 (December 2000): 45-48. Available at www.si.umich.edu/~presnick/papers/cacm00/reputations.pdf/.

24. "More Than 2.5 Billion Cellular Lines in the World," Geekzone.com (September 7, 2006). Available at www.geekzone.co.nz/content.asp?contentid=6628.

25. Hong Kong Office of the Telecommunications Authority, May 2006. Available at http://www.ofta.gov.hk/en/datastat/key_stat.html.

26. "Multifunctional Mobiles Make the World Go Round," Nokia press release, June 6, 2006. Available at www.nokia.com/A4136001?newsid=1054096.

27. "Latest African Mobile and Cellular Statistics," Cellular Online. Available at www.cellular.co.za/stats/stats-africa.htm.

28. By 2003 there already were twice as many mobile phones (53 million) in use in Africa as there were land lines (25.1 million). See Esharenana E. Adomi, "Mobile Phone Usage Patterns of Library and Information Science Students at Delta State University, Abraka, Nigeria," *Electronic Journal of Academic and Special Librarianship*, 7, no.1 (spring 2006). Available at http://southernlibrarianship.icaap.org/content/v07n01/adomi_e01.htm

29. *What the World Thinks in 2002: How Global Publics View: Their Lives, Their Countries, The World, America,* Pew Global Attitudes Project, December 4, 2002. Available at http://pewglobal.org/reports/pdf/165.pdf.

30. David Ignatius, "From 'Connectedness' to Conflict," *Washington Post* (February 22, 2006), A15. Available at www.washingtonpost.com/wp-dyn/content/article/2006/02/21/AR2006022101148.html.

31. For a more detailed description of the Estonian voting system, see www.vvk.ee/elektr/docs/Yldkirjeldus-eng.pdf.

APPENDIX

Forum on Communications and Society (FOCAS)
Annual CEO Meeting

Next Generation Media: The Global Shift

The Aspen Meadows Resort • Aspen, Colorado
August 9-12, 2006

Forum Participants

Richard Adler
Research Affiliate
Institute for the Future

Madeleine Albright
Principal
The Albright Group

Zoë Baird
President
John and Mary R. Markle
  Foundation

Yochai Benkler
Professor of Law
Yale Law School

John H. Clippinger
Senior Fellow
Berkman Center for Internet
  and Society
Harvard Law School

Ted Cohen
Managing Partner
Tag Strategic, LLC

Jeffrey I. Cole
Director
Center for the Digital Future
Annenberg School for
  Communication
University of Southern
  California

Lance Conn
Executive Vice President
Vulcan, Inc.

Charles M. Firestone
Executive Director
Communications and
  Society Program
The Aspen Institute

Note: Titles and affiliations are as of the date of the conference.

Dan Glickman
Chairman and Chief Executive
 Officer
Motion Picture Association
 of America

Jordan Greenhall
Chief Executive Officer
 and Founder
DivX, Inc.

Peter Hirshberg
Chairman and Chief
 Marketing Officer
Technorati

Reed E. Hundt
Senior Advisor
McKinsey & Company

Funmi Iyanda
Funmi Iyanda Productions

James Kelly
Managing Editor
Time Inc.

Robert McDowell
Commissioner
Federal Communications
 Commission

Marc Nathanson
Vice Chair, Charter
 Communications and
Vice Chairman, National
 Democratic Institute for
 International Affairs (NDI)
 and
Chair, Mapleton Investments

Craig Newmark
Founder and Customer Service
 Representative
craigslist

Joseph Nye, Jr.
Distinguished Service Professor
John F. Kennedy School
 of Government
Harvard University

Cory Ondrejka
Chief Technology Officer
Linden Lab

Deven Parekh
Managing Director
Insight Partner Ventures

John W. Rendon
President
The Rendon Group

Lynda Resnick
Co-Owner and Vice-Chairman
Roll International Corporation

Christopher Sacca
Head of Special Initiatives
Google, Inc.

Kwaku Sakyi-Addo
Information Specialist
 and
Broadcaster, BBC World Service
 and Joy FM, Ghana

Daniel Schorr
Senior News Analyst
National Public Radio

Note: Titles and affiliations are as of the date of the conference.

Arthur Sulzberger, Jr.
Chairman
New York Times Company
 and
Publisher
New York Times

Tracy Westen
Chief Executive Officer
Center for Governmental Studies

Clay Thomas Whitehead
Distinguished Visiting Professor
 of Communication Policy
George Mason University

Staff:

Mridulika Menon
Senior Project Manager
Communications and
 Society Program
The Aspen Institute

Note: Titles and affiliations are as of the date of the conference.

About the Author

Richard Adler is principal of People & Technology, a research and consulting firm based in California's Silicon Valley. He also is a research affiliate at the Institute for the Future (IFTF) in Palo Alto, California.

He was one of the first staff members of the Aspen Institute Communications and Society Program, serving as Associate Director under Douglass Cater, the Program's founder. He also has written reports on several Aspen conferences over the past decade.

He has taught communications at Stanford University and UCLA and was a research fellow at the Harvard Graduate School of Education.

His recent publications include "Anytime, Anyplace Health: How Mobile Applications are Expanding Access to Healthcare" (IFTF, 2006); "Reinventing Retirement" (*Aging Today*, 2005); "The Age Wave Meets the Technology Wave: Broadband and Older Americans" (SeniorNet, 2004); and "Telecommunications 2010" (Institute for Information Policy, 2001).

He holds a BA from Harvard, an MA from the University of California at Berkeley, and an MBA from the McLaren School of Business at the University of San Francisco.

Previous Publications
from the Aspen Institute
Forum on Communications and Society

Soft Power, Hard Issues (2005)

Shanthi Kalathil, rapporteur

In this compilation of two reports, the author explores the growing importance of soft power by looking at two crucial areas of international tension: the U.S. role in the Middle East and Sino-American relations. The role of information and communications technologies in American public diplomacy in the Middle East and American's relations with China is a central theme in the reports. 70 pages, ISBN: 0-89843-447-5, $15.00.

Opening the Realm: The Role of Communications in Negotiating the Tension of Values in Globalization (2005)

Michael Suman, rapporteur.

Opening the Realm addresses how communications media and information technologies can be used to ameliorate or exacerbate the tensions among the values of peace, prosperity, and good governance or among the forces of security, capitalism, and democracy. That is, can the media help a society gain the simultaneous benefit of all three values or forces? How does one prioritize how the media go about doing that in a free society? What is the role of the new media, which has so much promise to involve the individual in new ways? 51 pages, ISBN: 0-89843-432-7, $15.00.

Media Convergence, Diversity and Democracy (2003)

Neil Shister, rapporteur.

In the summer of 2002, chief executive level leaders from the public and private sectors met at the Aspen Institute to address the underlying role of media in a democratic society and policies that may improve the ability of citizens to exercise their roles as informed sovereigns in that society. This publication, authored by journalist Neil Shister, examines the concern of many over the shrinking electorate in American elections and the possible role the mass media play in that trend, the debate over whether consolidation in old and new media raises "democratic" as opposed to antitrust concerns, and opportunities for new media to enable citizens to communicate—both in terms of gaining new information and exchanging their own opinions with others. He also addresses the concern that new media will become bottlenecked rather than continue the open architecture of the Internet. 56 pages, ISBN: 0-89843-374-6, $12.00.

In Search of the Public Interest in the New Media Environment (2001)
   David Bollier, rapporteur.
   This report examines public interest and the role of the marketplace in redefining this concept with respect to educational and cultural content. It suggests options for funding public interest content when all media are moving toward digital transmission. The publication also includes afterthoughts from an international perspective by British historian Asa Briggs. 61 pages, ISBN Paper: 0-89843-333-9, $12.00.

Information Literacy: Advancing Opportunities for Learning in the Digital Age (1999)
   Richard P. Adler, rapporteur.
   This report explores the barriers that impede acquisition of the knowledge and skills needed to effectively manage information in its myriad forms, especially digital. It explores six concrete initiatives that individuals and institutions might develop to remedy this problem. The report includes a background paper on information literacy by Patricia Senn Breivik, former dean of libraries at Wayne State University and chair of the National Forum on Information Literacy. 45 pages, ISBN Paper: 0-89843-262-6, $12.00.

Jobs, Technology, and Employability: Redefining the Social Contract (1998)
   Richard P. Adler, rapporteur.
   This report examines the changing nature of the employee-employer relationship and whether the economic, technological, demographic, and social trends driving the global economy will lead to the development of a new "social contract" between employer and employee. 62 pages, ISBN Paper: 0-89843-241-3, $12.00.

Creating a Learning Society: Initiatives for Education and Technology (1996)

Amy Korzick Garmer and Charles M. Firestone, rapporteurs.

The first report of the Aspen Institute Forum on Communications and Society offers a range of initiatives for overcoming barriers to funding technology in schools and training teachers to integrate technology into the classroom. 81 pages, ISBN Paper: 0-89843-197-2, $10.00.

Reports can be ordered online at *www.aspeninstitute.org* or by sending an email request to *publications@aspeninstitute.org*.

About the
Communications and Society Program
www.aspeninstitute.org/c&s

The Communications and Society Program is an active venue for global leaders and experts from a variety of disciplines and backgrounds to exchange and gain new knowledge and insights on the societal impact of advances in digital technology and network communications. The Program also creates a multi-disciplinary space in the communications policy-making world where veteran and emerging decision-makers can explore new concepts, find personal growth and insight, and develop new networks for the betterment of the policy-making process and society.

The Program's projects fall into one or more of three categories: communications and media policy, digital technologies and democratic values, and network technology and social change. Ongoing activities of the Communications and Society Program include annual roundtables on journalism and society (e.g., journalism and national security), communications policy in a converged world (e.g., the future of video regulation), the impact of advances in information technology (e.g., "when push comes to pull"), advances in the mailing medium, and diversity and the media. The Program also convenes the Aspen Institute Forum on Communications and Society, in which chief executive-level leaders of business, government and the non-profit sector examine issues relating to the changing media and technology environment.

Most conferences utilize the signature Aspen Institute seminar format: approximately 25 leaders from a variety of disciplines and perspectives engaged in roundtable dialogue, moderated with the objective of driving the agenda to specific conclusions and recommendations.

Conference reports and other materials are distributed to key policymakers and opinion leaders within the United States and around the world. They are also available to the public at large through the World Wide Web, *www.aspeninstitute.org/c&s*.

The Program's Executive Director is Charles M. Firestone, who has served in that capacity since 1989, and has also served as Executive Vice

President of the Aspen Institute for three years. He is a communications attorney and law professor, formerly director of the UCLA Communications Law Program, first president of the Los Angeles Board of Telecommunications Commissioners, and an appellate attorney for the U.S. Federal Communications Commission.